E OUT ANY

LOCKING SHIELDS!

BRAIN SPEFD

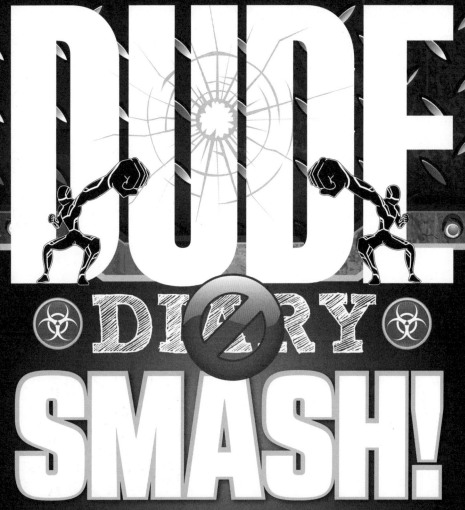

DUDE DIARY SMASH!

WRITE STUFF! DRAW RANDOM THINGS! DESTROY IF NEEDED!

DUDE DIARY
SMASH!

CREATED BY
MICKEY AND CHERYL GILL

FINE print
PUBLISHING

Fine Print Publishing Company
P.O. Box 916401
Longwood, Florida 32791-6401
www.fprint.net

Created in the USA & Printed in China
This book is printed on acid-free paper.

ISBN 978-1-892951-82-3

2 3 5 7 9 10 8 6 4 1

thedudebook.com

SMA

YOU'VE BEEN DROPPED FEET FIRST INTO A DEATH-DEFYING QUEST.

LOAD UP A HIGH-TECH JET PACK.

BATTLE A BRIGADE OF OFFENSIVE FOOD.

MAP OUT ALIEN INVASION HIDING PLACES.

LET THE PERILOUS JOURNEY **BEGIN!**

WHAT DO YOU DOMINATE?
(a.k.a. something you're great at)

[   ]

DANGEROUS animal that would make an EPIC pet for you?

Something COOL that you made with your own 2 hands?

☐

☐

☐

☐

Know any KARATE moves?

☐ Not really
☐ Of course
☐ I'm kind of an expert.

How would you describe your **eyebrows?**
☐ **Pretty average** ☐ **Thin**
☐ **Bushy** ☐ **Threatening**

JOB you'd like to have in the FUTURE?

☐ Extraterrestrial Interpreter
☐ Emperor of Awesomeness
☐ Roller Coaster Tester

☐ Robot Crimes Investigator
☐ Unexplained Phenomenon Photographer
☐ Couch Money Collector

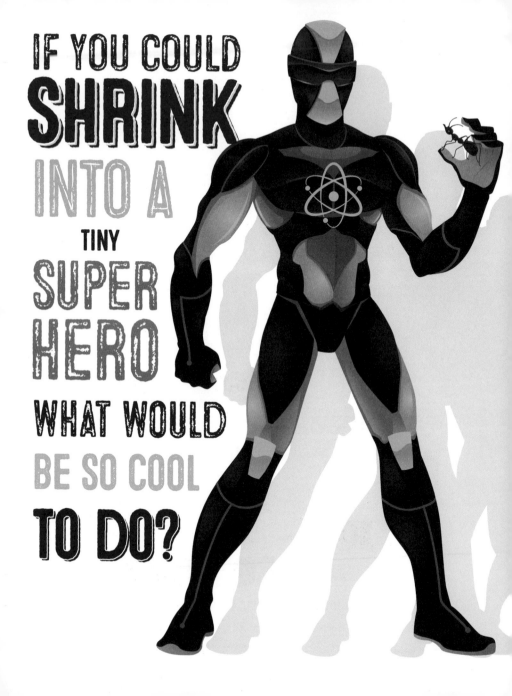

WHOA!
IT'S A FLYING CHAMELEON!

WHAT OTHER ANIMAL FEATS WOULD BE REALLY CRAZY? ➡

IT WOULD BE AMAZING IF ...

1. A(N) _____ COULD _____.
   ANIMAL   COOL TRICK

OUTTA THE WAY DUCKS!

2. A(N) _____ COULD _____.
   ANIMAL   COOL TRICK

3. A(N) _____ COULD _____.
   ANIMAL   COOL TRICK

4. A(N) _____ COULD _____.
   ANIMAL   COOL TRICK

5. A(N) _____ COULD _____.
   ANIMAL   COOL TRICK

IF A TELEPATHIC EXTRATERRESTRIAL WERE TO READ YOUR MIND TODAY, WHAT WOULD IT DISCOVER?

ARE YOU MORE OF A ☐ SUPERHERO ☐ SIDEKICK?

WHAT KIND OF **FOOD TRUCK** WOULD BE **EPIC TO RUN?**

FAMOUS PERSON YOU'D LIKE TO MEET? ⬇

Food Truck Name

A(N) ☐ ELECTRIC SNAKE ☐ SABER-TOOTHED FERRET ☐ KILLER BUTTERFLY WOULD BE THE COOLEST!

IS SO NOT OK!!

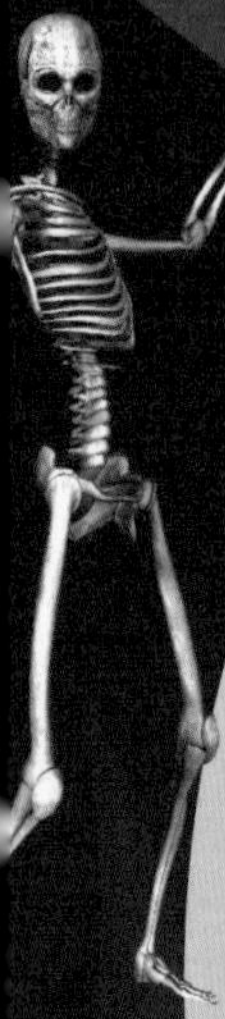

YOU & YOUR BROS HAVE THE MOST GIMUND SKILLET IN THE WORLD

WHAT WOULD BE AWESOME TO FRY UP?

ASK YOURSELF. ASK YOUR FRIENDS. SEE WHAT YOUR DOG WOULD LIKE.

1.

2.

3.

4.

5.

6.

7.

8.

WHAT WOULD YOUR NICE, SWEET VOICE TELL YOU TO DO TODAY?

WHAT WOULD YOUR STINKY, MISCHIEVOUS ONE TELL YOU?

SUPER NICEST THING YOU'VE EVER DONE?

SOMETHING "NOT COOL" YOU DID THAT YOU WISH YOU COULD UNDO?

WOULD YOU RATHER
HAVE A PAIR OF GLASSES WITH

☐ X-RAY VISION   ☐ TIME-TRAVEL CAPABILITY

You'd see for miles! ◁   ☐ BIONIC POWERS   ☐ LASER VISION?   *You'd see the future!*

WHY? AND WHAT WOULD YOU DO WITH YOUR POWER?

_____

_____

_____

_____

_____

_____

_____

What did you shovel into your mouth today?

↙ List it here.

Now, draw everything you ate between the teeth of this food tube hole. ↘

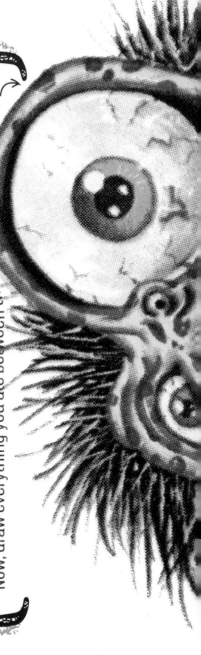

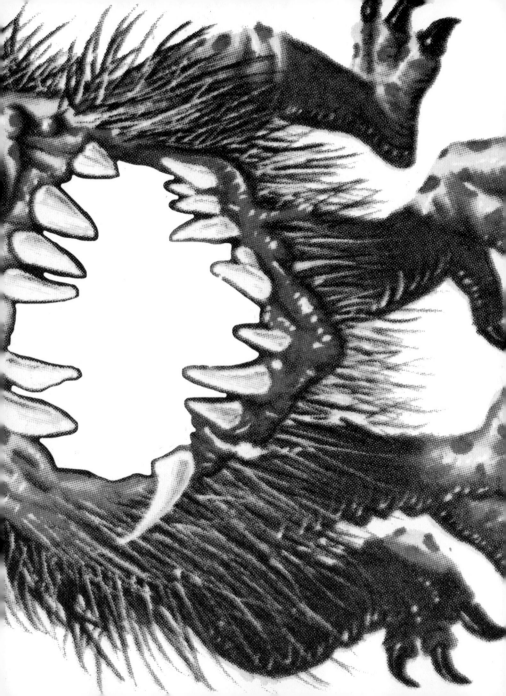

IF YOU COULD
EMPTY YOUR HEAD
OF USELESS INFORMATION,
WHAT WOULD YOU DRAIN OUT OF YOUR BRAIN?
THEN, WHAT WOULD YOU FILL IT WITH?

Do I really need to remember the right way to load the dishwasher?

I need the plans for an underwater community embedded into my brain.

I'd fill my head with applesauce!

START AN
URBAN
LEGEND

[A STORY ABOUT AN UNUSUAL EVENT THAT MANY PEOPLE BELIEVE IS TRUE BUT IT'S NOT.]

FILL IN THE DETAILS.

SO MY FRIEND'S MOM WAS DRIVING US HOME FROM

_____

_____ ONE NIGHT WHEN I

SAW A _____

_____ RISING UP OUT

OF A _____ .

IT HAD _____

_____ , AND THEN

IT _____

_____

_____ .

AN ELEVATOR TO ~~~~~ WOULD BE MIND-BLOWING!

☐ FUDGE BALLS
☐ A GIANT CHEESE BALL
☐ PEANUT BUTTER BALLS

WOULD SATISFY MY HUNGER RIGHT NOW.

WOULD YOU RATHER BE A
☐ ZOMBIE HUNTER
☐ LOCH NESS MONSTER researcher?

HOW DO YOU LIKE YOUR HOT SAUCE?

☐ MILD
☐ MEDIUM
☐ HOT
☐ TONGUE-MELTING

WHAT WOULD BE A TOTALLY CRAZY PHONE APP?

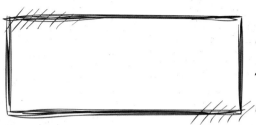

WHAT REALLY BUGS YOU ABOUT ADULTS?

WOULD YOU RATHER HAVE

☐ HANDS **THAT GRILL MEAT**
☐ EYES **THAT SEE BEHIND U**
☐ SLIME POOL**-PRODUCING BOOGERS?**

WHICH DO YOU TOTALLY need?

☐ **ROCKET LAUNCHER**
☐ **DRONE**
☐ **TANK**

CELEBRITY WHO'D BE COOL TO GAME WITH?

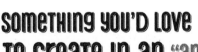

SOMETHING YOU'D LOVE TO CREATE IN AN "ANYTHING'S POSSIBLE" LAB?

You own a
skyscraper!
What awesome businesses will you fill it with?

I'm starting my own company making window-washing robo-spiders.

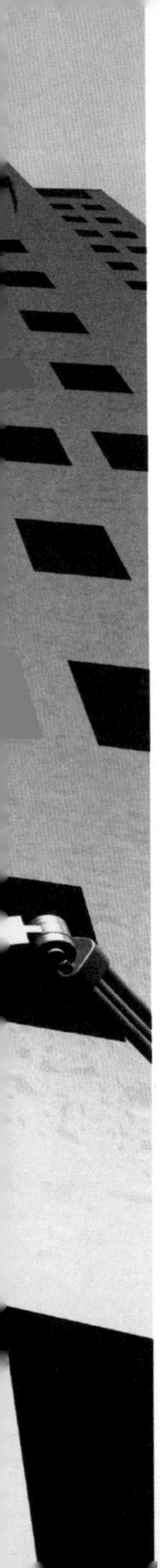

1. _____

2. _____

3. _____

4. _____

5. _____

6. _____

7. _____

8. _____

9. _____

10. _____

I want Big Bertha's Barbeque Sauce in my building!

A blood bank on the ground floor would be nice.

WHAT DO YOU DO THAT FREAKS

OUT YOUR PARENTS, TEACHERS, FRIENDS, AND NEIGHBORS?

WHAT WOULD BE SO COOL TO SMASH!

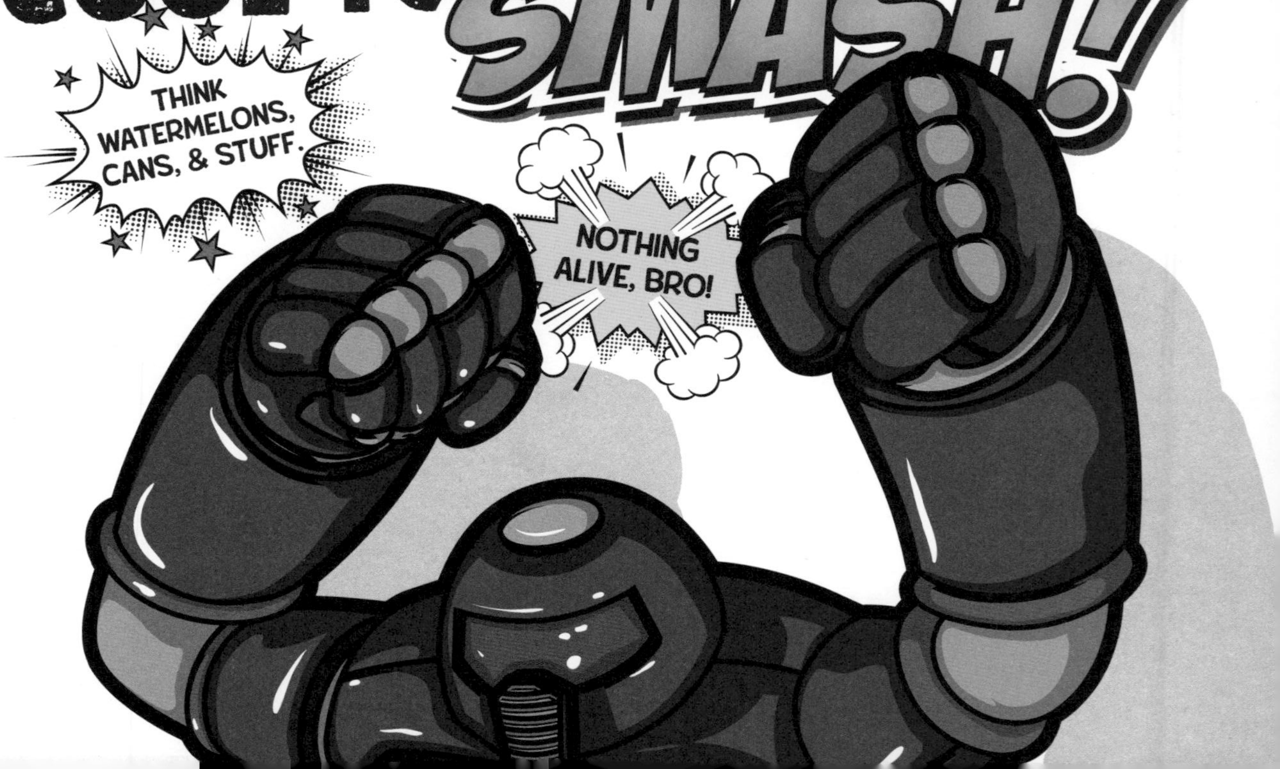

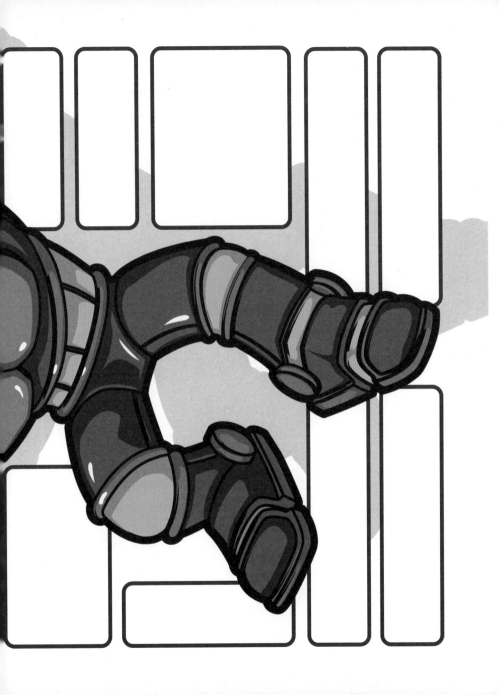

1. [   ]

2. [   ]

3. [   ]

4. [   ]

5. [   ]

My sister and her boyfriend kissing.

I find hairless cats repulsive.

IF THERE WERE AN ALIEN INVASION, A ZOMBIE APOCALYPSE, OR A SWEATY STENCH MIST COVERING THE EARTH, WHERE WOULD YOU HIDE?

TOP 10 HIDING PLACES?

1. _____

2. _____

3. _____

4. _____

5. _____

6. _____

7. _____

8. _____

9. _____

10. _____

WHICH LAND ANIMALS WOULD BE EPIC IN THE OCEAN?

ANIMALS ➤➤➤➤ NOW GIVE THEM A NEW NAME

_____   _____

_____   _____

_____   _____

_____   _____

_____   _____

As in
awesome!

WHICH SEA CREATURES WOULD BE SICK ON LAND?

ANIMALS ➤➤➤➤ NOW GIVE THEM A NEW NAME

_____   _____

_____   _____

_____   _____

_____   _____

_____   _____

WOULD YOU RATHER

BE CHASED BY A ☐ FANGED SEA SERPENT
☐ GIANT VAMPIRE BAT?

LIVE WITH A ☐ PACK OF MONKEYS THAT ONLY EAT BANANAS
☐ BUNCH OF BANANAS THAT ONLY EAT CHICKEN?

HAVE INITIALS THAT SPELL ☐ P.O.O. ☐ W.E.E.?

WORK IN A ☐ DONUT SHOP ☐ PIZZA PALACE?

OWN ☐ AN INVISIBLE RAT ☐ TELEPORTING PARROT?

FLY TO ☐ THE MOON ☐ AN UNEXPLORED PLANET?

WIN A SHOPPING SPREE TO ☐ AN OUTDOOR STORE
☐ GAMING STORE?

BE ☐ PRESIDENT OF THE USA ☐ A MOVIE STAR?

☐ WORK IN THE SEWERS
☐ WASH SKYSCRAPER WINDOWS?

←DRAW TECH ON PACK

YOU SCORED A **TECH PACK!**

NOW LOAD IT UP WITH **HIGH-TECH GADGETS.**

[JET TECH IS ALREADY INCLUDED.]

WRITE DOWN YOUR
GADGET REQUEST LIST

TODODAY IS _Sunday_ ,&
Date

I AM ...

PSYCHED
ABOUT →

DREADING ↙

SCARING ↓

PLAYING

STUDYING →

PRANKING

GOING TO ↓

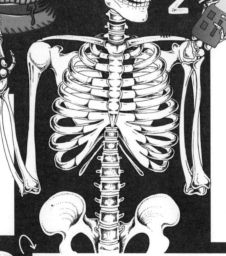

EAT ING ↘

LISTENING 2 →

DAR ING ↰

 TO

_____
Name

_____
Dare

THE GOVERNMENT HAS ASKED
YOU TO DIRECT A TEAM OF SU

NAME

NAME

PERHEROES

ASSIGN THEM NAMES & DESIGN THEIR UNIFORMS.

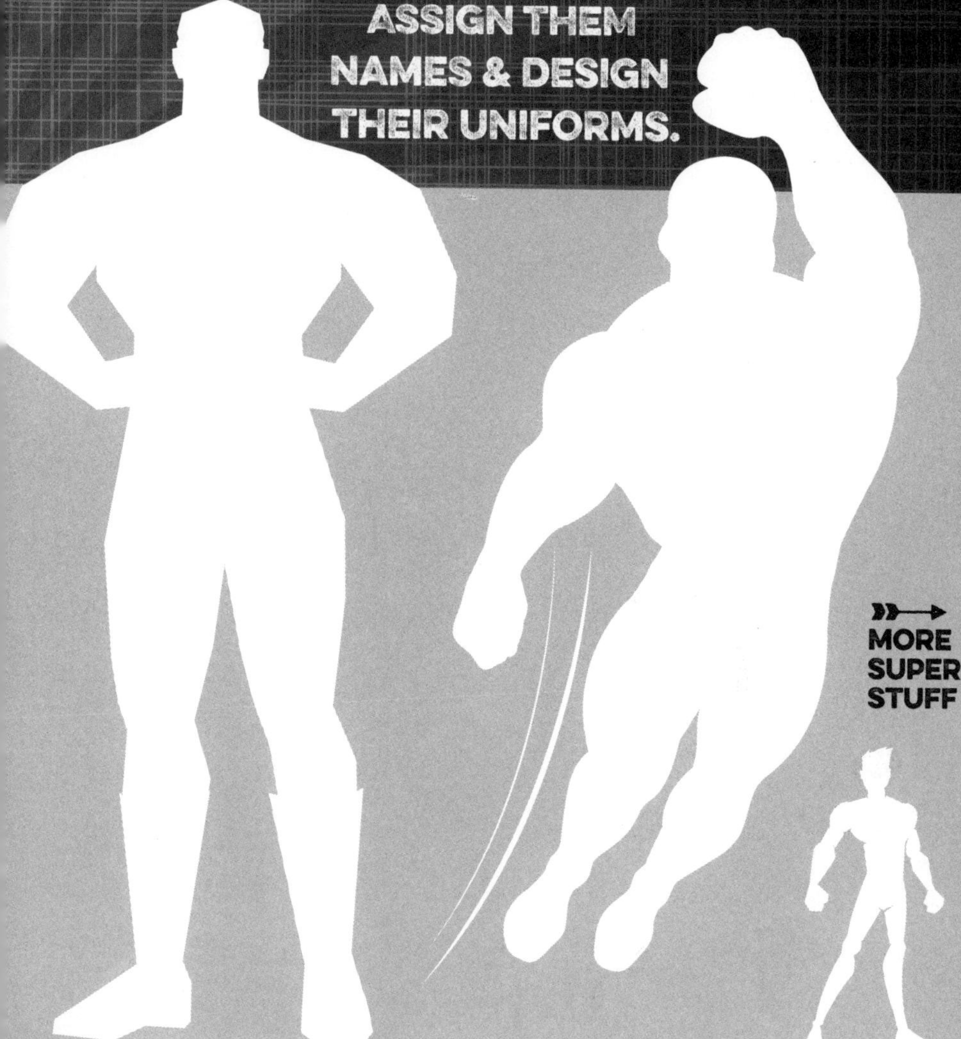

MORE
SUPER
STUFF

NAME

NAME

NAME

THE TEAM OF
SUPERHEROES
NEEDS A NAME

COMBINE SOME OF THESE WORDS TO CREATE ONE.

TEAM	AMAZING	DEFENDERS	PEACE
LEAGUE	AWESOME	POWERS	JUSTICE
CREW	DYNAMIC	GUARDIANS	SECURITY
PATROL	MEGA	PROTECTORS	FUTURE
LEGION	ULTRA	FIGHTERS	UNIVERSE
FRIENDS	SUPER	CHALLENGERS	GALAXY
SQUAD	WONDER	WARRIORS	FREEDOM
CORPS	INCREDIBLE	CHAMPIONS	TROUBLE
FORCE	SUPREME	COMMANDOS	CHAOS

[   ]

SUPERHERO TEAM NAME

NOW,
DESIGN A LOGO OR
SYMBOL FOR YOUR TEAM.

[IT WILL GO ON YOUR SUPERHERO TEAM HEADQUARTERS.]

WHY? WHAT WOULD YOU WANT TO FIND OUT?

WHAT WOULD BE

REALLY FUNNY OR SUPER GROSS TO FILL A GINORMOUS BALLOON WITH BEFORE POPPING IT?

What makes your BRAIN hurt
just thinking about it?

FRIED
- ☐ Cheese curds
- ☐ Chicken strips
- ☐ Shrimp?

Would you rather have a
PIRATE'S
■ peg leg   ■ hook hand?

What/who do you need to
CONQUER?

☐ My fear of

_____
Fear

☐ _____ in _____
Friend's Name   Video Game Name

Would you rather have a ROBOTIC
☐ hive of bees   ☐ army of ants?

Which 2 HEROES
should team up to take on which 2 VILLAINS?

_____ & _____	VS	_____ & _____
Heroes		Villains

IF YOU HAD THE POWER TO HYPNOTIZE PEOPLE,
WHO WOULD YOU HYPNOTIZE?

WHAT RiDiCULOUS THiNGS WOULD YOU WANT THEM TO DO?

Hypnotize — make people really sleepy and then tell them things to do.

_____

_____

_____

_____

_____

_____

_____

_____

Look into my eyes. Now, bark like a dog.

RUFF!

You need a T with a lot of SWAG!

←DRAW IT.

WHAT AMAZING, EPIC, CRAY-CRAY, OR COMPLETELY NORMAL THINGS DO YOU HOPE TO BE DOING WHEN YOU'RE...

16
YEARS OLD?

_____
_____
_____
_____

25
YEARS OLD?

_____
_____
_____
_____

30
YEARS OLD?

_____
_____
_____
_____

50
YEARS OLD?

_____
_____

70
YEARS OLD?

_____
_____

UNDERGROUND SPACE
HAS OPENED UP FOR
YOUR DUDE CAVE.

DRAW EVERYTHING YOU'LL NEED IN IT.

WHAT WOULD MAKE WATCHING TV 1000 TIMES MORE INCREDIBLE?

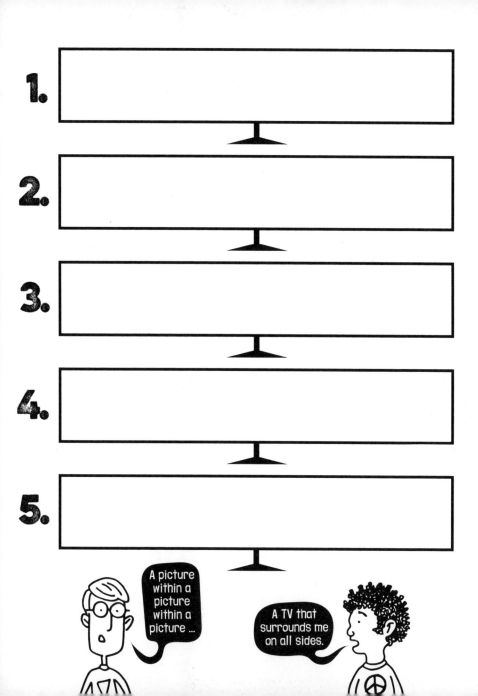

IF
YOU
HAD A
GiANT
ERASER
WHAT WOULD YOU
LOVE TO ERASE?

IT'S GOOD VS. EVIL IN

1. DESIGN THE GALAXY
Draw the planets and name them. Add stars, suns, moons, or something completely different.

UNIVERSE FAR AWAY.

AND YOU GET TO CREATE IT!

2. DESCRIBE OR DRAW

the aliens, humanoids, creatures, or other organisms that live on each planet.

DO YOU NEED TO EVACUATE YOUR SNIFFER?

□ NO,
IT'S
SQUEAKY
CLEAN.

□ YES,

IT'S
FULL OF

SICK!
Looks like a
small community
of organisms. And
dude, they're busy.

It's prob
just full
boogers and dus

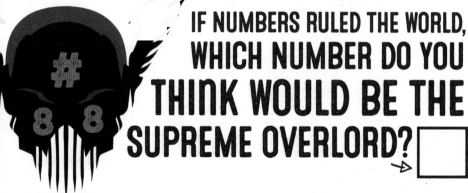

IF NUMBERS RULED THE WORLD, WHICH NUMBER DO YOU THINK WOULD BE THE SUPREME OVERLORD?

WHAT MEAL COULD YOU EAT THREE TIMES A DAY FOR THE REST OF YOUR LIFE?

WHAT SHOULD BE YOUR CATCH PHRASE?
☐ PREPARE TO BE VANQUISHED!
☐ WHAT UP FISH LIPS?
☐ UNLEASH THE KRAKEN!

ANIMAL YOU WISH COULD TALK TO YOU?

WOULD YOU RATHER BE *SUPER*
☐ STRONG ☐ SMELLY ☐ HAIRY
☐ SMART ☐ FUNNY ☐ STRETCHY?

BEST THING IN THE FROZEN FOOD AISLE?

WORDS YOU & YOUR FRIENDS USE A LOT → TRANSLATE → WORDS IN YOUR NEW LANGUAGE

_____   _____

_____   _____

_____   _____

_____   _____

_____   _____

_____   _____

_____   _____

_____   _____

_____   _____

_____   _____

SLOTH ROCKET

epically slow

Really fast

What else would be way better if it were way faster?

1.

2.

3.

4.

5.

MAKE AN UNBELIEVAE

INCLUDE SOME HAZARDS LIKE AN ALLIGATOR POOL
or snake PIT. WHOA!

Draw THe rest OF THe course

DIRT BIKE COURSE!

Write your own bedroom rules.

'S RULES

Your name

1.

2. NO

3.

4.

5. ALWAYS _____

6. _____

7. _____

8. _____

9. _____ IS NOT ALLOWED AT ANY TIME.

10. _____

IF YOU HAVE TO GO TO SCHOOL IT SHOULD BE COOL, RIGHT?

HOW WOULD YOU TRICK OUT YOUR CLASSES?

SCARY MOVIE POPCORN!!!

Why should the movie have all the fun?! What would be funny, disgusting, or frightening to cover popcorn with?

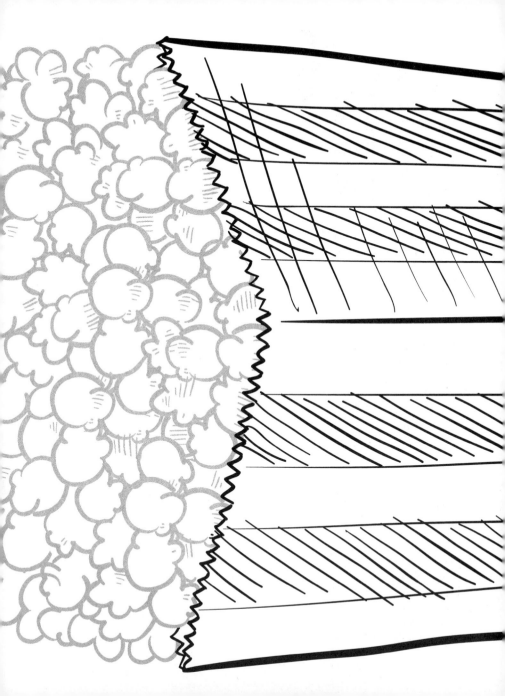

WHAT

would you want to talk to through a

HOLOGRAPHIC WATCH?

[   ]

WHICH WORD ADDED TO YOUR FIRST NAME WOULD MAKE IT WAY MORE AWESOME?

☐ DIESEL
☐ GATOR
☐ CRANKSHAFT

WHOSE DREAMS WOULD BE HILARIOUS TO ENTER?

[   ]

WHAT'S SCARIEST?

☐ Balloon animals   ☐ Fiber bars
☐ Tongue scrapers   ☐ Adult diapers

Most annoying word girls use?

☐ Totes ☐ Cute ☐ Adorbs   ☐ Other_____

WHAT FOODS LIKE TO TA

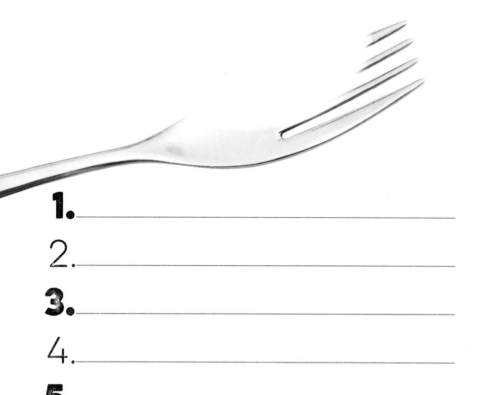

1. _____

2. _____

3. _____

4. _____

5. _____

OULD YOU
KE DOWN?

DRAW THE **WORST** ONE
ON THE FORK.

Wheat grass juice, carrot juice, apple juice. YAWN. What would be crazy cool to send through a turbo juicing machine?

1. _____

2. _____

3. _____

4. _____

5. _____

6. _____

7. _____

8. _____

9. _____

10. _____

The smashed bugs off my dad's car.

A bunch of scrap metal.

IF YOU HAD ABSOLUTELY ZERO FEAR
WHAT WOULD YOU DO?

1. _____

2. _____

3. _____

4. _____

5. _____

6. _____

7. _____

8. _____

9. _____

10. _____

NEED A team OF _____ _____ TO HeLP Me

WANT TO Be THe **1ST DUDE** TO _____

WISH I COULD REMOVE MY _____ @ ANY TIME.

THINK MY friends anD I COULD Be in charge OF _____

WOULD LIKE TO HaVe a Jar FULL OF _____

I'm pretty sure we could be in charge of Mars.

Oh yeah, piece of cake.

Planet Earth is really lucky to have you.
What makes you SO COOL?

I can let one rip & burp at the same time.

I always make sure no fry is left behind.

Were sent to detention for flinging mac 'n cheese at a friend?

WHO WOUL

WITH YOU IF YOU...

WeRE HEADED TO an **ALL-YOU-Can-eat** CHICKEN WINGS BUFFET?

ENTERED a NATIONAL GAMING CONTEST?

WERE TRYING TO HIDE AN ANCIENT DINOSAUR EGG (THAT'S ABOUT TO HATCH) FROM THE WORLD?

NEEDED TO FIND HOMES A.S.A.P. FOR A LITTER OF KITTENS?

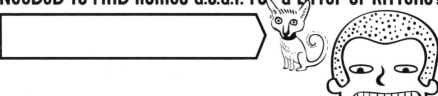

Had to perform in a skit in front of the entire school?

YOU WANT

HAD TO TAKE YOUR NEIGHBOR'S VICIOUS DOGS FOR A WALK?

WERE DODGING GIANT CHEESE BALLS FROM OUTER SPACE AS THEY CRASHED THROUGH THE 🌎'S ATMOSPHERE?

HAD TO TIE ONE OF YOUR LEGS TO SOMEONE ELSE'S FOR **an entire DAY?**

NEEDED TO SOLVE A RIDDLE TO SAVE ALL MANKIND?!

TURN HERE TO ENTER A DOMAIN WHERE YOU ARE INDESTRUCTIBLE.

WRITE DOWN YOUR NEXT PLAN OF ATTACK.

DRAW THE UGLIEST CREATURE EVER IMAGINED.

CAUSE SERIOUS PAPER DAMAGE.

SMASH STUFF BETWEEN PAGES.

THERE ARE NO FORTIFIED CITIES, FORCE FIELDS, OR TOWERS OF POWER TO STOP YOU FROM SENDING STRONG MENTAL MESSAGES FROM YOUR MIND TO YOUR HAND.

BRO, YOU OWN THIS.

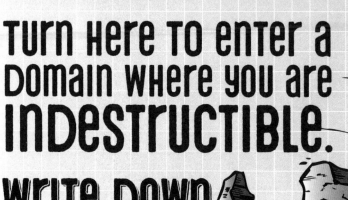

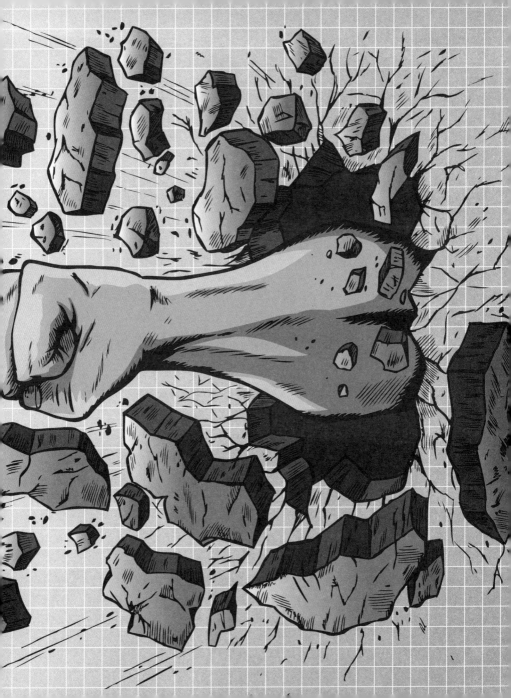

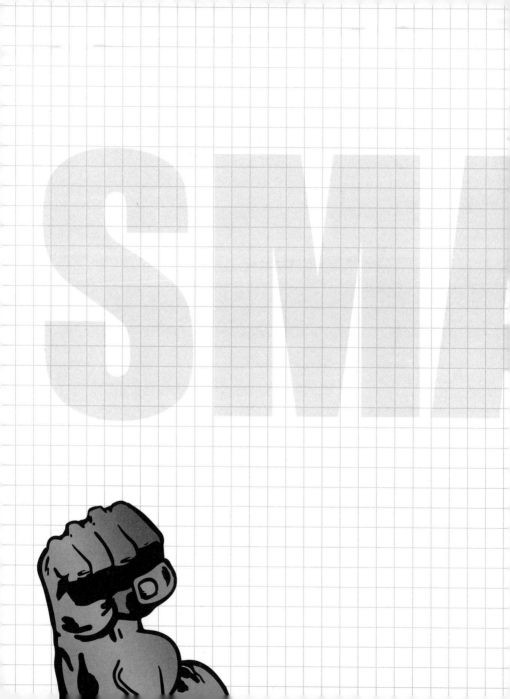

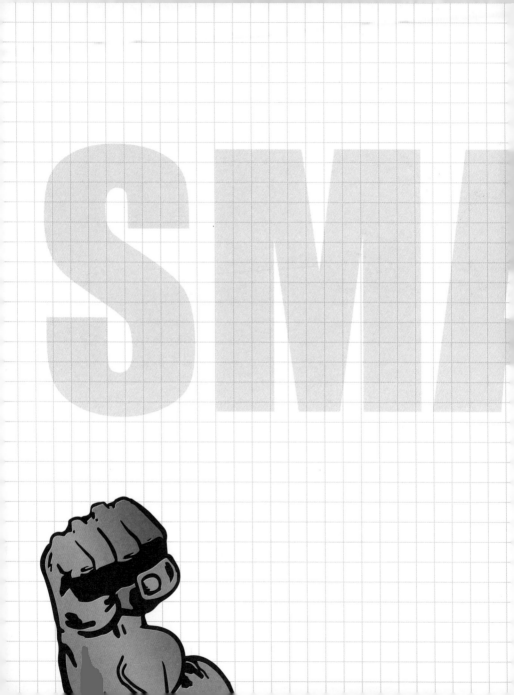

MIND BLO